# The Basic Essentials of
# AVALANCHE SAFETY

## by Buck Tilton

**Illustrations by**
**Marc Bohne**

ICS Books, Inc.
Merrillville, Indiana

# THE BASIC ESSENTIALS OF AVALANCHE SAFETY

10 9 8 7 6 5 4 3 2 1

Printed in U.S.A.

## DEDICATION

A work of nonfiction is never the result of one individual's effort. Indebtedness for this book goes to those who have researched, compiled, written, edited, and taught during the preceding years. Thanks especially to Betsy Armstrong, Tony Daffern, Doug Fesler, Colin Fraser, Ed LaChapelle, Rod Newcomb, and Knox Williams. And, with great appreciation and fondness, thanks to Ken Thompson.

**Published by:**
ICS Books, Inc.
One Tower Plaza
107 E. 89th Avenue
Merrillville, IN 46410
800/541-7323

**Library of Congress Cataloging-in-Publication Data**

Tilton, Buck.
    The basic essentials of avalanche safety / by Buck Tilton ;
        p.  cm. -- (The basic essentials series)
    Includes index.
    ISBN 0-934802-84-X : $5.99
    1. Avlanches--Safety measures    I. Title.   II. Title: Avalanche
    safety.
QC929.A8T55  1992
613.6--dc20                             92-21091
                                           CIP
                                           r92

# TABLE OF CONTENTS

# 1. THE SEASON OF SNOW AND DANGER

"I never fear that any avalanche will catch me unless I have myself brought it down." Unknown Swiss guide, 1936.

10 January 1962. An earthquake shakes North Huascaran, a 21,000 foot peak in the heart of Peru. A huge chunk of the glacier hanging from the summit breaks off. The resulting ice avalanche picks up tons of rock from the mountainside. Averaging an estimated 36 miles per hour, the torrent travels approximately 10 miles, involves somewhere near 80 million cubic feet of ice, and sweeps away many tilled fields, thousands of domestic animals, and more than 4,000 human lives. Miraculously the village of Yungay, though it lay in the path of destruction, is spared by a small hill that diverts the avalanche. This is the first great avalanche is Peru's history, but it is not the last.

On 31 May 1970 another earthquake shakes Mount Huascaran, triggering the release of a second tremendous avalanche. This one thunders over Yungay's protective hill, destroys the village, and ends more than 20,000 human lives. This is the most destructive avalanche the world has yet known.

It is unlikely a town in North America will ever experience devastation equal to Yungay's. Avalanche potential, created by a combination of snow conditions, terrain, and weather, does not exist in the extremes found in South America except, perhaps, in Alaska and parts of Canada where people are few and far between.

In the United States, the single worst avalanche disaster occurred on 1 March 1910. Two westbound trains of the Great Northern Line, one carrying passengers and the other mail, were stopped by a huge avalanche on 23 February in the Cascade Mountains near Wellington, Washington. Snow continued to fall through two days and nights of effort to unblock the tracks. On 26 February snow intensity reached a foot per hour, and a second avalanche slid across the tracks. Passengers huddled in the trains. On 1 March the snow turned to rain, and a third avalanche, one-half mile long, one-quarter mile wide, and 20 feet deep, pushed both trains off the tracks, burying them under tons of wet snow. 22 people were left on the surface or uncovered by rescuers. 96 people died.

In Canada the worst disaster occurred on 22 March 1915 when 57 people were killed in a mining camp in British Columbia.

Between one and two dozen people will die beneath avalanches in the United States each year. Three to five times that number will die in European avalanches during the same time period. Who are these people? They are mountain travelers. Backcountry ski tourers, downhill skiers, and climbers are the most common victims. Skiers are especially susceptible because the most appealing places to ski are the most likely places to avalanche. Most of the victims are unable to identify high risk terrain and unstable snow conditions, and some get caught up in the excitement that snow breeds . . . and forget. They trigger the slides that kill them.

There is little mystery to an avalanche. As with earthquake, fire, and flood, avalanches have no mind and no will. They are simply awesome power, elemental force. When there is a slope, a sufficient load of snow, and a triggering nudge, an avalanche occurs.

Avalanches are any masses of significant proportions in motion down the side of a mountain. They are sometimes referred to as slides, and may be composed of rocks, mud, or dirt, but, unless otherwise stated, the word "avalanche" is generally accepted to mean a mass of sliding snow. They vary from small sluffs, or sloughs, that run no more than 50 yards to gigantic climax avalanches that involve entire mountainsides and millions of tons of snow. Interestingly, most mountain travelers are killed in avalanches that slide between 50 and

100 yards. Whatever their size, all avalanches will fall into one of two types, determined by the character of the snow at the origin of the slide.

A loose snow avalanche, one type, originates at a single point, or in a small area, and fans out as it moves downhill. The snow within a loose snow avalanche is... loose, with poor cohesion among the crystals. Sometimes it is so loose you cannot detect a line separating the snow that avalanched from the snow that stayed put. Loose snow will slide when the angle of the slope is overly steep for the snow crystals to stick. These avalanches typically have little destructive power except in the warmer months when they may be substantially wet.

**Figure** 1-1 Loose-Snow Avalanche

A slab avalanche, the other type, starts when a large mass of snow breaks away all at once and occurs when cohesion is high. There is an obvious fracture line, called the crown, where the slab separates from the more stable snow cover underneath. Sometimes fracture lines mark the sides of the avalanche's path. At the lower end of the slab, where it breaks away from and overrides the stable snow, you will find a line of failure called the stauchwall. After the avalanche subsides, a distinguishable ledge or shoulder usually marks the stauchwall. The cohesive layer, or slab, may slide along the ground, but it usually slides on a less cohesive layer lying beneath it. This less cohesive layer, called the lubricating layer, provides the bed surface, or gliding surface, upon which the avalanche rides. Slab avalanches may be soft or hard. Soft slabs break apart after starting to slide, taking on the appearance of a large, loose snow avalanche. Hard slabs tend to break into blocks of snow that retain some of their angularity. Slab avalanches create the greatest source of life-threatening danger in snowy mountains.

**Figure** 1-2 Slab Avalanche

Terrain determines the path the avalanche will follow. Avalanche paths can be divided into three zones. The release zone, as the name implies, is where the avalanche starts and picks up speed. Along the track, the middle zone of the path, the snow slides at a relatively constant speed, unless altered by bold terrain changes, and little or no snow is deposited. Below the track lies the deposition zone where the snow decelerates and finally stops.

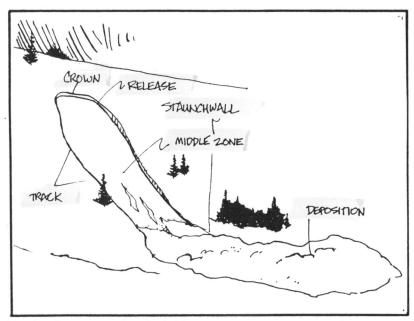

**Figure 1-3** Anatomy of an Avalanche

When snow has fallen to a sufficient depth, and when the cohesion between layers of snow or between snow and ground grows loose enough, and when the slope is steep enough, the snow will avalanche. As with the equalizing burst of electrical energy called lightning, avalanches are another way in which all things seek a natural balance. And, as with lightning, it is impossible to know exactly when an avalanche will strike. But you can make a well-educated guess. Unless someone above you kicks loose an avalanche, you will probably trigger the slide that kills you. That leaves two options for those who want to be safe: 1) learn to recognize and evaluate and avoid avalanche danger, or 2) stay home.

# 2. KNOWING THE SNOW

"The experienced mountaineer learns to judge snow conditions with marvelous accuracy and becomes so confident of his opinion that he will risk his life on his judgement." F. A. Collins, 1923.

When did human and snow first meet? Perhaps three million years ago in Africa, in the heights of the Ruwenzori Range, or on Mount Kilimanjaro. Assuredly snow was a factor in the lives of people one-half million years past, as the Great Ice Age creeped across Europe. But avalanches were rarely, if ever, a problem for the ancients. They had no reason to travel to the country of the avalanche-beast, to the land of white fury.

Hannibal was the first avalanche victim to be noted in written history. As a military maneuver, he attempted to cross the Alps, in the winter of 218 BC, with 38,000 soldiers, 8000 horses, and about three dozen elephants. Fresh snow fell heavily on an old, hard crust as Hannibal's army crossed an unknown pass. An avalanche, or avalanches, wiped out one-half his men, one-fourth his horses, and several elephants. Such are the fortunes of war.

Snow falls on the prepared and the unprepared. During the winter of 1970-71, a record 1027 inches fell on Paradise in Mount Ranier National Park. In one month, January 1911, 390 inches fell on Tamarack, California. A single storm, lasting from 13-19 February 1954, dropped

189 inches into Mount Shasta Ski Bowl. In one 24-hour period, in April 1921, a 76- inch thick blanket covered Silver Lake, Colorado.

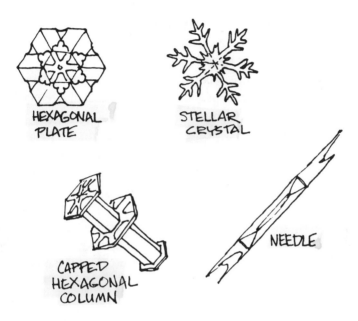

HEXAGONAL PLATE

STELLAR CRYSTAL

CAPPED HEXAGONAL COLUMN

NEEDLE

**Figure 2-1** Types of Snow Crystals

When the temperature drops below freezing and water vapor condenses into crystals, snow falls. Cold, still air usually produces feathery plates or soft stars, the lightest snow, falling with infinite grace and beauty. Stars are the loveliest form of snow, but they are not the most common. As the mercury rises, the snow becomes harder, forming needles, columns, and, most commonly, irregular clumps. Near freezing temperatures may produce balls of snow called sleet, a hard shell with a soggy center, or hail, which is solid ice, often striking the earth with ruinous force. Each successive storm lays down another layer of snow. The accumulated layers are called the snow cover, or snowpack. The snowpack meets the atmosphere at a boundary called the snow surface. Where the snow cover meets the ground is called the ground surface.

## Snow Metamorphism

Snowpacks change, or metamorphose, with time. Metamorphism is constant, altering the form and structure of the snow crystals from the moment they land on earth until the moment they have completely melted. Successive layers of snow, falling under differing weather conditions, metamorphose at different speeds depending on the temperature changes that accompany each storm. Eventually, the snow cover stratifies into distinct layers, and the cohesion between layers is a major factor in determining if the snow will avalanche.

Snow metamorphism is controlled primarily by temperature, happening quickly near freezing and stopping almost altogether below minus 40 degrees Fahrenheit. Pressure also participates in metamorphism, causing snow deep in the snow cover to change faster than snow near the surface. When solid water changes into water vapor without going through the liquid stage, the process is called sublimation. Sublimation plays another key role in snow metamorphism.

When there is a relatively constant temperature throughout the snow cover, the crystals, whatever their original form, become more and more round. Through sublimation, solid water at the ends of the crystals changes to vapor and refreezes near the center of each crystal. Each snow crystal, intricate and distinct, is doomed to become a tiny rounded grain. This is called equi-temperature (ET), or destructive, metamorphism. The grains stick tightly to each other forming a very cohesive layer.

When temperatures within the snow cover vary, water vapor tends to spread out through the snow, moving along the temperature gradient, from the warmer snow close to the ground toward the colder snow at the surface. When the conditions are met, entirely new snow crystals are formed. The new forms appear as cups or scrolls, and may reach several thousandths of an inch in diameter. This new snow is called hoar. Hoar deep in the snowpack is called depth hoar. On the surface, it is called, appropriately, surface hoar. The greater the temperature differences within the snow cover, and the greater the permeability of the snow, the greater the formation of hoar. This is called temperature-gradient (TG), or constructive, metamorphism. Depth hoar is fragile, collapsing easily into a very non-cohesive, lubricating layer.

TG layers form easiest in the early season when the snow cover is thin and the temperature difference between the ground and the snow surface is greatest. TG layers are common at high altitude where the snow surface grows colder and a greater gradient is created between surface and ground. Higher elevations tend, also, to be windier and to avalanche more often, both of which keep the snow thinner and gradient greater.

When snow melts and then refreezes, it forms an icy layer that may become a slippery sliding surface for snow deposited in later storms. This is sometimes referred to as melt-freeze (MF) metamorphism. If the melt phase is long enough for water to percolate down through the snow to the ground, a lubricating layer can cover an entire mountainside.

A tightly bonded layer on top of a weakly bonded layer creates the basic prerequisite for a slab avalanche.

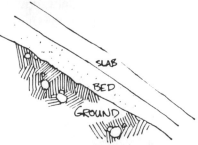

**Figure** 2-2 Avalanches require a cohesive layer on a noncohesive layer.

## Snow Mechanics

Wind is the greatest mechanical disturber of snow. When snow is disturbed by wind, then allowed to set, it hardens. Old, wind-

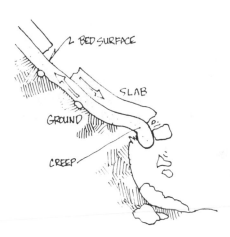

**Figure** 2-3 Creep

hammered snow may be as much as 50,000 times harder than fresh, powder snow. Wind-hardened snow forms an extraordinarily cohesive layer, one that may slide easily off an underlying weak layer.

Snowpacks developing on slopes undergo another type of mechanical deformation. This deformation occurs because of snow's elasticity (the ability to stretch and return to the original shape) and viscosity (the resistance to flowing freely), and the weight of gravity. Snow tends to flow, or "bend," downhill, a movement called creep. And snow tends to slide downhill along the slope, a movement called glide. As with metamorphism, creep and glide are affected by temperature. Snow has minimum viscosity near the freezing point. As the temperature drops, viscosity increases and creep and glide slow down. The stresses created within the snow cover by uneven creep and glide add more factors in determining if the snow will avalanche.

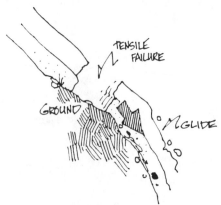

**Figure** 2-4 Glide

## Safety Summary

The snow cover evolves constantly. The amount of metamorphosis is relative to temperature between layers, pressure on buried layers, and mechanical changes due to wind and gravity. Of primary importance in determining the stability of the snowpack are 1) the depth of the snow, 2) the strength of the layers within the snow, and 3) the degree of bonding between the layers. These observations can be made and analyzed by digging a pit in the snow cover (See Chapter Five).

# 3. INTERPRETING THE TERRAIN

"Accurate appraisal of snow conditions takes training, experience, and a good source of observational data, but the recognition of avalanche terrain can be easily learned." E. R. LaChapelle, 1985.

Any snow-covered slope steep enough to slide may, and victims have been caught and killed in avalanches on a great variety of terrains. But certain types of mountain terrain are especially dangerous. The most basic avalanche safety skill is the ability to recognize avalanche-prone terrain.

Important factors in the creation of dangerous terrain include the profile of the slope (is it straight, convex, concave?), the inclination of the slope (how steep is it?), irregularities in the slope (gullies, ravines, bowls, terraces, benches, outcroppings, canyons, ridges), the ground surface underneath the snow (grass, bushes, boulders, trees), and the orientation of the slope (to sun and wind).

## Slope Profile

Any straight slope, open and covered in snow, is an avalanche waiting to happen, and the slide may start anywhere on the broad, smooth surface. If the slope is convex, flexed up toward the sky, the chance of an avalanche is even greater. That convex bulge enhances tensile stress, a stretching tension created within the mass of snow by its tendency to creep downhill. The weight of a lone skier may be enough to trigger the release of the tension. A crack will occur at the point of highest stress, usually just below the bulge, and the snowpack will slide downhill.

A concave slope is generally considered safer than a convex slope. Hard snow at the bottom of the slope supports the snow higher up. But all is not necessarily well. Soft snow or snow resting on depth hoar at the bottom of a concave slope may give, with the weight of a traveler, upsetting the snow balance on the slope above and causing it to slide.

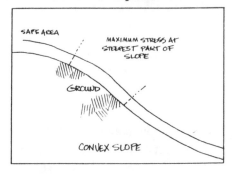

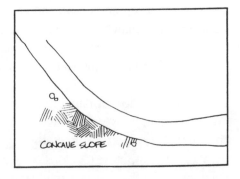

**Figure** 3-1 Convex vs. Concave Slope

## Slope Inclination

How steep must a slope be to avalanche? Wet, sloppy avalanches have occurred on slopes as shallow as 15 degrees. This type of slide would seldom be dangerous, unless it pushed you over a cliff. Wind-hardened slabs have fallen off mountainsides as steep as 60 degrees, but snow on terrain that steep usually sluffs off before it consolidates into avalanche proportions. The majority of death-dealing avalanches occur on slopes that fall in the range of 30 to 45 degrees. Studies indicate a pronounced tendency for snow to slide in the 35 to 40 degree range.

How steep is that slope? There are two ways to judge the angle of a slope. Relatively accurate measurements can be taken with an inclinometer. Easy to use and inexpensive, an inclinometer is a lightweight piece of plastic, usually manufactured with directions printed on the face.

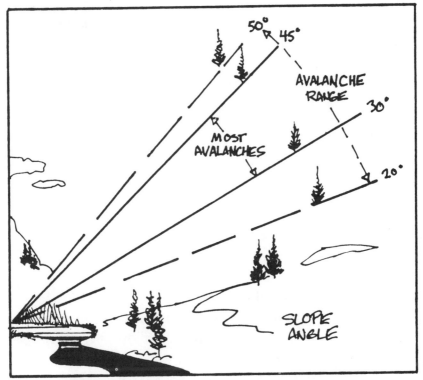

**Figure 3-2** Most avlanches slide on inclines of 30-45 degrees.

Relatively inaccurate guesses can be made as to slope angle. The simplest guess-method requires you to hold your hand with the index finger and thumb at a right angle, and line up the slope where the finger and thumb meet. If the slope approximately divides the 90 degree angle of finger and thumb, the slope is roughly 45 degrees. Steeper slopes will lie closer to your index finger, gentler slopes closer to your thumb. Fortunately, almost everyone overestimates slope angle, guessing the slope is considerably steeper than it really is.

## Slope Irregularities

Gullies, or narrow ravines, form natural pathways for snow to slide down. Climbers are especially susceptible to gully

avalanches since gullies also form natural pathways up a
mountain. The release zone above the gully, where storms may

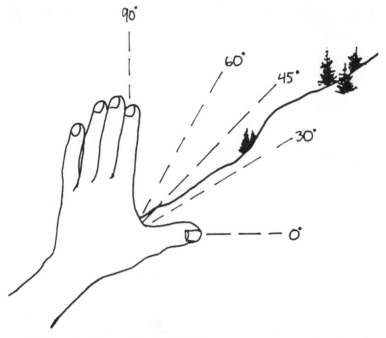

**Figure** 3-3 Rough estimate of a slope's incline.

have deposited a huge mass of snow, is difficult, often impossible,
to evaluate from below. A gully, even a shallow one, on an open
slope, is a perfect place for snow to deposit and consolidate into a
tense, avalanche-prone slab.

Snow-filled bowls create insidious traps for the unwary. Their
beautifully sloping sides are a Siren's call to skiers, but those same
sides trap heavy snow deposits which harden and avalanche easily.
Bowls often have narrow outlets where the sliding snow builds up. An
avalanche starting on a wide slope and funnelling into a gully offers an
opportunity for you to be buried deeply.

Terraces, or benches, form natural barriers to an avalanche . .
. until the snow builds up to a sufficient depth to create a straight
slope over the terrace. Early in the snow season a terrace is a
tempting path for the mountain traveler, but the same terrace may
create a deposition zone for a slide from above, and a burial
ground for the unwary.

An outcropping of rock, forming an island of refuge, may be a safe stopping place in an avalanche zone. Far better to avoid the avalanche zone altogether.

Wide canyons often offer safe routes of travel. Narrow canyons often form death traps as avalanching snow piles up in the bottom. The questions to answer are 1) how much snow is on the sides of the canyon?; 2) how stable is the snow cover?; and 3) how wide is the runout zone? Stay well away from sloping, snow-covered sides.

Ridges offer the safest routes. The wider the ridge, the safer the ridge. The narrower the ridge, the greater the chance for a cornice to form. Cornices are overhanging lips of snow created by wind. The lip of snow "grows" from the ridgetop out in the direction of the prevailing wind, so the cornice overhangs the leeward side of the ridge, the side sheltered from the wind. Cornices often hide from a traveler on the ridge. It is safer to travel on ridges on the windward side, the side facing the wind, away from the possibility of cornices. And avoid traveling under a cornice. They sometimes break off naturally, triggering an avalanche.

### Slope Surface

Underneath the snow, the surface of the slope adds to the factors determining if the snow will slide, especially early in the season. As a general rule, the rougher the slope surface, the more snow it takes to

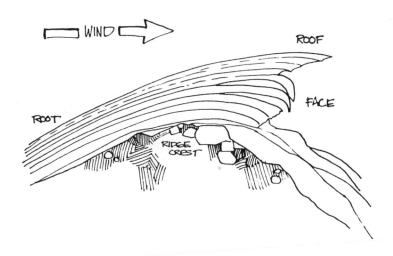

**Figure 3-4** Cornice

create an avalanche. Each successive layer of falling snow reduces the adhesive effects of the ground underneath the snow.

Grassy slopes and smooth rock surfaces will avalanche easily. These surfaces, if they are steep enough, will often avalanche to the ground several times during the snow season.

Bushes and small trees, such as willows, will usually anchor the snowpack early in the season. But later, under heavy snow, light vegetation is crushed by the weight and bent downhill by the creep of the snow cover, and, thus, adds very little to snow stabilization. Dense vegetation may actually trap air near the ground, encouraging the formation of depth hoar, and helping provide a weak layer as a bed surface for an avalanche.

Trees, if they are thin enough to ski easily through, will not deter an avalanche. Slopes covered with thick timber, however, trees virtually impossible to ski through, are usually safe. But look above the timber, taking note of the possibility of a huge slab breaking off of an open slope with enough mass to destroy the tree cover.

## Slope Orientation

Mountains have faces, and the orientation of a mountain's face to sun and wind helps determine if the snow cover will slide. In the Northern Hemisphere, south slopes are the ones facing south and getting the full force of the sun. North slopes lay in shadow during most of the day. Windward slopes are those facing into the wind, and leeward slopes are those whose faces are hidden from the wind.

Since south slopes get more sunlight, snow metamorphism progresses at a faster rate than on north slopes. Snowpacks consolidate quicker after a storm, making them either avalanche soon after a storm or stabilize sooner, both of which, generally, make south slopes a safer bet for travel during the mid-season. But later in the season, as temperatures rise and snow begins to melt, south slopes are prone to wet avalanches, and the risk of traveling on them increases.

North slopes, getting little sunlight, remain cooler with resulting retardation in metamorphism. Cooler temperatures also increase the chance of depth hoar formation, and the persistence of that weak layer. So north slopes remain dangerous longer after a storm, but they maybe safer toward the end of the season when wet snow is sliding off the south faces.

Latitude has an effect on both slopes. Southern south faces, such as those in the southern Rocky Mountains, get more solar radiation than slopes with the identical orientation in the northern Rockies. Greater radiation creates a higher rate of recrystallization of the snow which tends to produce more thin, weak layers that form sliding surfaces for avalanches. Colorado has more avalanches than similar altitudes in Canada. But on Canada's northern north slopes the snow clings longer and avalanche danger persists longer.

Wind, playing an extraordinarily important role in the formation of avalanches, demands attention. Wind moves snow around, and, once disturbed, the snow hardens into slab avalanche consistency. The mountain traveler needs to be aware of the wind's prevailing direction to avoid avalanche-prone slopes. When wind can be felt or blowing snow can be seen, the job of determining wind direction is an easy one. Just remember to keep a high awareness level. In the absence of wind, mountains offer more subtle reminders of where the wind once blew. Cornices, like a windsock at an airport, point the wind's direction. Sometimes swirling winds create double-corniced ridges with windsocks in both directions. Double cornices are useless frustrations in determining wind direction. Around trees, rocks, and other things that stick out of the snow, the wind will build drifts. Wind piles up snow on the windward side of objects, and long tails stretch out on the leeward side of these drifts, pointing the wind's direction. On open surfaces, hard winds may carve sastrugi in the snow. Sastrugi describes the eroding effect persistent wind has on snow. The steeper, sharp faces of sastrugi point into the wind, the broader tails fan out on the leeward side. Ice crystals carried on the wind will sometimes collide with supercool moisture on the surface of something sticking out of the snow, building fantastic towers of icy snow called rime. Rime always builds up on the windward side of objects, pointing into the prevailing wind. The amount of rime and the taller the rime, the higher the wind.

Windward slopes, slopes that face into the wind, will have less snow deposited on them than lee slopes. The snow will be tightly compacted and, thus, usually safer.

In the wind, leeward slopes will gather snow quickly, whether there is fresh snow falling or not. Rapid snow deposition makes lee

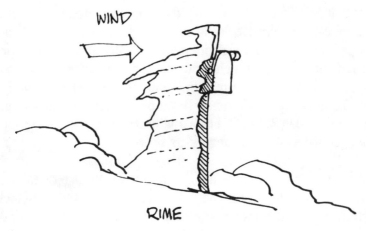

**Figure** 3-5  Rime

slopes far more unstable and dangerous for travel than windward slopes. Lee slopes avalanche naturally far more often than windward slopes. Stay on the windward side of life.

## Pathways of the Past

Finally, terrain that once sustained an avalanche is the place where an avalanche is most likely to occur again. Keep an eye open for steep, open mountainsides, and bare swaths of snow cutting through a stand of timber, and stands of saplings running through an older forest, and steep gullies with no growth in them. Look out for trees that are torn and scarred, with limbs ripped off on the uphill side, and tops missing. Watch for piles of dirty snow, with debris and uprooted trees mixed in, at the bottom of slopes. Check slopes ahead for fracture lines where an avalanche started but lacked the impetus to continue on down.

## Safety Summary

Observe the profile of the slope ahead. Generally, convex slopes are very dangerous, straight slopes are dangerous, and concave slopes are the least dangerous. Check the slope's inclination. Slopes of 30 to 45 degrees are dangerous, however slopes of 35 to 40 degrees are the most dangerous. Stay out of gullies, ravines, bowls, and narrow canyons. Wide canyons are usually safe, but along the tops of ridges are safer. Avoid leeward slopes, especially if they have overhanging cornices. Watch for evidence that the slope has avalanched before. Sometimes the dead people found beneath avalanches overlooked the obvious. Avoid avalanche terrain.

# 4. WEATHER OR NOT

"Only fools and dudes predict the weather." Paul Petzoldt, 1965.

Gravity, that force making the ascent of mountains most difficult, holds the earth's atmosphere close enough to the surface to make mountaineering, and life itself, possible. The atmosphere is approximately 21 percent oxygen. Mixed with the oxygen is nitrogen, and a variety of other gases in much smaller amounts. Floating among the gases are incredibly small particles of such stuff as sea salt, dust, and volcanic ash. The tiny particles form an anchor for another constituent of the atmosphere, water vapor. Water vapor is densest where the atmosphere is densest, closest to the earth's surface, and close to the earth, in the lower atmosphere, is where most weather occurs.

The pressure of the atmosphere, called the barometric pressure, is greatest at the surface of the earth, where the atmosphere is densest. As the altitude of the earth's surface goes up, the pressure, for the most part, goes down. At 18,000 feet above sea level, the barometric pressure is only one-half what it is at sea level. For weather determination, however, it is important to note that the actual barometric pressure varies up and down with the movement of large masses of air.

Nature consistently attempts to maintain a balance in all things. As air near the earth's surface heats up, it expands and its density goes down. The warming air, now growing lighter in pressure, rises until it reaches a point of equilibrium with the surrounding air. As the temperature of air increases, so does the amount of moisture it can carry. Rising air carries its moisture, in the form of water vapor, up. As warm air rises, it begins to cool. Eventually it will cool to the point where it grows dense enough to begin to fall. Thus the air is dynamic, moving up and down constantly. This is called convection. Air movement is confused by the rotation of the earth which tends to pull the circulating airmasses over on their sides.

It is the upward movement of air, with the water vapor it contains, that most concerns the mountain traveler. Moisture in the air must reach appreciable amounts for precipitation to fall. Convection is largely responsible for lifting moisture in the warmer months of the year, and, therefore, it is largely responsible for rain. In the colder months, convection plays only a small role in lifting moisture. Airmasses, and their moisture, get high during the colder months in three other ways: cyclonic circulation, frontal lifting, and orographic lifting.

Around a low pressure area on the earth's surface, the air always circulates in a counterclockwise direction. (It reverses in a high pressure area.) Airflow is concentrated toward the center of the low pressure area, and the air in the center rises. This is called cyclonic lifting. (This, too, is reversed in a high pressure area, where air sinks in the center.) In lower latitudes, cyclonic lifting may produce the majority of cold weather precipitation. In higher latitudes, especially in mountainous terrain, this form of lifting is often quite small.

**Figure** 4-1 Cyclonic Lifting

The boundary where one circulating airmass meets another circulating airmass is called a front. When one airmass is cold, say from the Arctic, and one is warm, from the Pacific, they will not mix when they meet. If the warm front is advancing to meet the cold airmass, it will rise gently over the cold air, carrying moisture which may fall gently. If the cold front advances to meet the warm air, the warm air is forced up quickly, carrying moisture which may fall heavily. This is called frontal lifting. Mountains often trap cold airmasses on their windward sides, increasing the frontal lift of warm airmasses.

Steeply rising terrain forces horizontally moving air to rise quickly. The faster the windspeed and the more sharply the terrain rises, the more quickly the airmass rises. This is called orographic lifting, and it may be ten times greater than either cyclonic or frontal lifting. The more quickly the airmass rises, the more quickly it cools. The more quickly it cools, the more rapidly its water vapor condenses. When the vertical lift of a moist airmass produces condensation to the point where the rising air can't hold the weight of the water droplets (rain) or frozen crystals (snow), they fall.

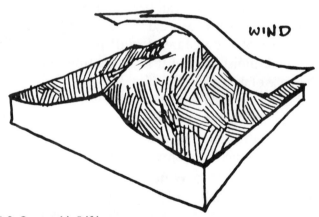

WIND

**Figure** 4-2 Orographic Lifting

If the speed and direction of the wind is known, and the moisture content of the airmass (the humidity), and the barometric pressure, and the temperature, then the weather can be predicted. But it is not weather prediction that the backcountry traveler needs to learn. It is, instead, an awareness of weather patterns and changes in weather that needs to be learned. Any change in weather causes a proportional change in the snow cover of the mountains. Those changes most influencing avalanche conditions are snowfall, wind direction and speed, and temperature changes.

## Snowfall

To evaluate the hazard of an avalanche in relation to snowfall, you need to know how much snow has fallen and how fast it is falling. The depth of freshly fallen snow is an indicator of how fast the snowpack is settling. The faster the settlement, generally, the tighter the bond and the safer the slope. The intensity of snowfall, the rate per hour, is an indicator of how fast avalanche-prone slopes are being loaded. The faster the load builds up, the more unsafe the slope. An intense snowfall, especially if the wind is high, accounts for periods of greatest avalanche danger.

Precipitation is thickest just below the clouds where the humidity is highest and the temperature is the coolest, which puts the condensation rate at its maximum. Therefore, higher elevations get heavier snowfall. Snowfall is also higher on the windward side of mountains where lift is greatest. Once past the summit of a mountain range, lift stops and precip fades away. It is important, however, to remember that swirling winds can deposit a heavy load of fresh, dangerous snow on any lee slope. And if a storm originates in a warm area, such as one of the oceans, it will probably be carrying considerably more moisture than if it comes from a relatively dry region, such as one of the poles.

If possible, you should stay in contact with the local weather bureau prior to a trip into snow-laden mountains. Often, in mountainous areas, these bureaus maintain an avalanche watch, and provide an excellent source of information (see Appendix).

## Wind

Second only to snowfall in determining if snow will slide is the wind. Fast-moving wind picks up snow, whether it is falling or just laying on the ground, and drops it when it slows down. Wind causes snow to fill depressions in the slope creating the difficult-to-detect-but-deadly small slab avalanches. Wind loads the snow to dangerous depths on leeward slopes. Wind-awareness is critical in the development of avalanche-awareness.

High winds cause snow crystals to collide in the air while falling, and tumble across the surface once they land. As snow is wind-beaten, crystals break up into smaller pieces, creating a denser, more cohesive snow cover. On windward slopes, wind tends to create a snowcrust that is hard and etched, sometimes fantastically, and the crust will crunch directly under the weight of a traveler. But on leeward slopes, wind-driven snow forms the extremely dangerous slab, usually with a smooth, roundish shape that settles, under the weight of a traveler, with a frightening "whoompf" and cracks reaching out over a large area.

At higher elevations, where there is less influence on moving airmasses by changes in terrain, wind tends to blow in the same direction most of the time. These air currents are termed prevailing winds. Prevailing winds help determine weather patterns for a particular geographic area. A cold, moist prevailing wind will likely deposit a heavy load of snow resulting in a high avalanche danger. A warm, moist wind (above freezing) produces a great risk of wet snow avalanche. A dry prevailing wind, sometimes called a Chinook, can remove snow quickly due to evaporation, and does not increase the chance of an avalanche. Information on prevailing winds is usually available from the local weather bureau.

At any elevation, wind can be altered by terrain, air temperature, and other changing factors. These winds are called local winds. Local winds can swirl fiercely across mountainsides with sudden changes of direction, sometimes producing phenomena such as the double-corniced ridge.

Mountains produce a particular type of local wind that influences the snow cover. These air movements are caused by the rapid cooling of air at night at higher elevations, especially over high plateaus, glaciers, and icefields. The cooler, denser air begins to slip down the mountainsides. Cold night breezes are the result. But in the extreme northern parts of the earth, these winds can grow quite strong.

Local winds are evaluated primarily by being there, observing the indicators (see Chapter Three), and making a sound judgement about the stability of the snow cover.

## Temperature

Exchanges of heat occur between the ground and the snow cover, within the snow cover itself, and between the atmosphere and the snow cover. Heat transfer at the ground-snow boundary is minimal. Within the snowpack, little heat transfer occurs when the snow is dry. As the wetness of the snow increases, so does the rate of heat transference.

Rain, percolating down through the snow, always warms the snow cover. Heat exchange for snow is greatest at the surface where the snow and atmosphere meet and where heat energy is traded constantly. Although the processes are complex, they can be simply stated relative to two processes: molecular heat transfer and radiative heat transfer. In the molecular process, if the air is warmer than the snow, the snow gains heat, and if the snow is warmer than the air, the snow loses heat.

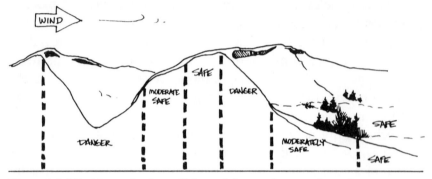

**Figure** 4-3  Wind is a major factor if determining a safe route of travel.

The molecular process is speeded up significantly by wind. The faster the wind, the faster the heat is exchanged. For the radiative process, the sun radiates heat to the snow, most of which is reflected and some of which is absorbed. Dry snow reflects more radiation than wetter snow. Radiation rates are also altered by the time of day, the day of the year, the orientation of the slope, and the thickness of the cloud cover.

Given the myriad possibilities, it is possible to only guess at the heat exchange of the snow cover. What is known for sure is that even small changes in temperature can make large changes in the character of the snowpack and its tendency to slide.

## Safety Summary

In short, it is possible to note a few very significant points. By far, the greatest number of avalanches occur during or just after a storm. A storm here can be either snow falling or already-fallen snow being moved around by strong winds. If the storm blows in warm and goes out cold, the new warm snow bonds well to the old surface, and the avalanche danger tends to be less. If the storm comes in warm and the temperature stays warm, but below freezing, consolidation continues and the stability of the snowpack increases. But if the temperature rises above freezing, the snow starts to melt and "wet" snow tends to slide easily. If the storm comes in cold and slips out warm, the bonding is poor between the new cold snow and the old surface, and the avalanche danger is correspondingly higher. If the storm comes in cold and it stays cold, the snowpack will break down internally and avalanche danger will persist a long time after a storm.

The rest of the analysis of avalanche danger is based largely on your ability to assess the terrain and its load of snow, and the stability of the snowpack. The most important questions are: 1) Which slopes are most heavily loaded? (Lee slopes gather the greatest load, with high winds packing the snow in isolated deep ravines and depressions.) 2) How much snow has accumulated? (Dangerous loads, generally, resulting from heavy snowfall and sustained winds.) 3) How fast has the load accumulated? (Rapid accumulation under high winds creating the greatest danger.)

Evaluating the stability of the snowpack is the subject of the next chapter.

# 5. EVALUATING THE HAZARD

"The only absolute rule in avalanche forecasting is... there are no absolute rules." Rod Newcomb, 1990.

When a patient is ill or injured, there is a Sherlock Holmesian search for clues before the rescuer can determine the appropriate response. Before a mountain traveler crosses suspect terrain, there must, likewise, be a search for evidence to determine the safety of the proposed route of travel. This evidence can be divided into the answers to four general questions A) What is immediately and directly observable about the stability of the snow cover? B) What can be discovered indirectly about snow stability by digging an investigative pit in the snow cover? C) What kind of weather has been contributing (and will contribute) to snow stability? D) What will be the probable outcome (for you) if the snow does come tumbling down?

## A. Directly Observable Evidence

If you witness an avalanche in the general area of travel, there is an immediate danger of another avalanche. Nothing should raise your level of suspicion more than seeing, or hearing, a nearby slide of snow. If there are fresh piles of tumbled snow, perhaps mixed with debris, at the foot of a slope, an unwitnessed avalanche has recently occurred, and the danger of another one, in that area, is high. If a fracture line has broken the tilted field of snow ahead, the snow has started to slide and subsided. An avalanche is probably just waiting for a mild disturbance to trigger it.

If the snow crunches around your skis or snowshoes, or cracks immediately underfoot, the snow is generally stable. If the cracks run out 20 or 30 or more feet ahead of the skis, or the snow makes that unsettling "whoompf" sound when weighted, the snowpack is unstable. When the snow speaks, listen! If skis, snowshoes or cramponed feet sink in little or none at all, the snowpack is very well consolidated. If they sink in up to your knees, the snow is unconsolidated. Dangerous slab formation is most often indicated by substantially hard snow or substantially soft snow. If the snow lumps on the bottom of boots or skis, the snow is wet. Wet snow can slide off a surprisingly low incline.

If tracks left behind you have firm neat walls, the snow is consolidating (ET-metamorphism). Good! The snow, at least the last layer to fall, is well bonded. If the walls of tracks fall in, or blocks of snow form between your feet and fall over, the snow is not consolidating (TG-metamorphism). Bad! The last layer to fall is poorly bonded. If the tracks are wet or ice-encrusted, there is a lot of water in the snow because it has melted or melted and refrozen (MF-metamorphism). Ugly! The whole mountainside is likely to slide off (see Chapter Two).

The important rules are 1) See the Snow, 2) Hear the Snow, 3) Feel the Snow.

Does the route of travel cross a type of terrain suitable for avalanching? (see Chapter Three) What is the slope's profile? Any straight slope can slide, especially if the snow is wet. Convex slopes have more internal stresses and are, therefore, more prone to sliding. Concave slopes are less prone to avalanche, but they can be triggered by failure of the supporting snow at the bottom of the slope. Is the slope steep enough to avalanche? Slopes in the 30 to 45 degree range are most likely to slide. Is the slope above the proposed route of travel in the highly suspect range? It might fail and avalanche the route of travel. Does the terrain create a natural pathway for an avalanche? A gully? A bowl? The path of an avalanche should not be the path of a traveler. Are there cornices above the route of travel? Change the route. What is the slope's orientation to wind and sun? Leeward slopes collect snow and are usually best avoided. Sunward slopes, especially those facing south and southwest, are exposed the strongest solar radiation. They tend to slide more easily, especially in the warming season.

Remember this important rule, Stay Tuned to the Terrain

### The Ski Pole Test

You can use a ski pole to perform a simple test that gives evidence about snow layers in the first three or four feet of snow. Push the basket end of the pole into the slope at a right angle to the incline. The push should be gentle, just enough to keep the basket moving against the resistance of the snow. A forceful or sudden stab of the pole will not allow you to feel changes in resistance. (If the snow is too resistant to a basket-first push, the pole can be reversed and the handle end pushed in first.) Push in as far as possible. And pull the pole out slowly, feeling the resistance of the snow against the basket's withdrawal.

The ski pole test may be used quickly and often, but it is not exhaustive. It is simply one of several indicators of the hazard. The ski pole test should be used near, but not out on the face of, a questionable slope. That would be dangerously silly!

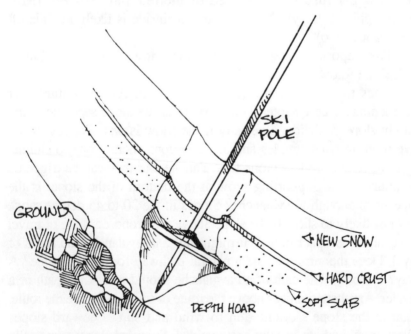

**Figure 5-1** Ski-Pole Test

## Interpreting the Ski Pole Test

Subjective evaluation is the bottom line for the ski pole test, but these guidelines should be generally helpful.

1) Little resistance means the basket is pushed in easily, the snow is unconsolidated, probably new snow or depth hoar.

2) Medium resistance means the basket took some effort to push in, the snow is consolidated, or perhaps a hardpacked windcrust.

3) Hard resistance means the handle end of the pole was used, the snow is compacted, a slab has formed.

4) Very hard resistance means the handle would not go in, a hard slab has formed.

5) Wet snow will let the basket in a few inches only, with increasing resistance and a wet feel and look.

6) The Best Case is the basket penetrating the snow with steadily increasing resistance and no especially hard or especially soft layers.

7) The Worst Case is meeting a resistant layer followed by a sudden breakthrough into a soft layer. This case deserves a closer look.

## The Shovel Shear Test

A ski pole is a useful tool for anyone traveling in avalanche country. A snow shovel should be considered a necessity. With a shovel you can perform the most important, readily observable test relative to snow stability. If the ski pole test, or some other evidence, indicates the possibility of a lubricating layer with a ready-to-slide mass on top of it, the shovel shear test can be used to determine the eagerness of the mass of snow to avalanche.

Any snow shovel will work, but ones with a wide, flat, metal blade work best. Without a shovel, a skier could use the tail of a ski. More work, but it will function. A snow saw is another relatively inexpensive, lightweight, highly-useful tool for the snow season traveler.

To perform the test dig a quick pit in the slope, to the ground or, at least, down through the last couple of snowfalls (four feet are generally enough). Be sure the upslope side of the pit is as vertical as possible. Cut a column out of the upslope side of the pit that is as wide and deep as the shovel blade (a job a snow saw makes fast and easy). Insert the shovel blade slowly and vertically into the back of the column to the full depth of the blade, and pull forward gently on the shovel handle. Watch for a plane of failure and the ease with which the column shears off and slides into the pit.

Choose a slope near the questionable area, and with the same orientation as the suspect slope, but, once again, not dangerously out on that slope.

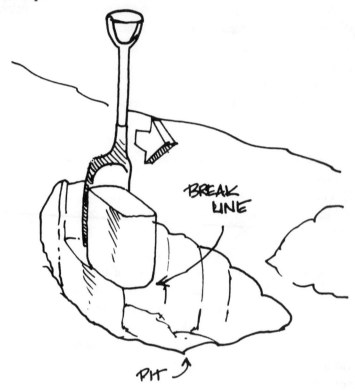

BREAK LINE

PIT

**Figure** 5-2 Shovel Shear Test

### *Interpreting the Shovel Shear Test*

As with the ski pole test, a certain amount of subjective judgement is required.

1) Difficult to get the column to shear off? Maybe it broke off rather than slid off. The shovel handle had to be pulled on with firm force. The snowpack is probably stable and safe to travel on. But ask yourself, will conditions remain the same along the proposed route of travel?

2) Moderate difficulty getting the column to shear off? It took

medium pressure on the shovel handle. A neat shear plane was evident. If the route of travel is steeper than the test slope, it will avalanche easier. If the route is less steep, it might be safe to travel on. The decision is not easy.

3) No difficulty getting the column to shear off? Minimum pull on the shovel handle was required. Shear plane very evident. The chance of a traveler triggering an avalanche is likely. Danger is high.

4) Extremely easy to get column to shear off? In fact, it failed without pressure on the shovel handle, or even before the shovel blade was inserted. The chance of natural avalanches is high. Danger is extreme.

## B. Indirect Evidence From the Pit

The length of time mountain travelers intend to spend in suspect terrain and the potential risk of a route will determine if there is need for the investigative pit and the indirect evidence it will give. The goals of digging a pit include determining if a slab has formed over a sliding layer, discovering the thickness of the snow cover, identifying the type of snow crystals involved, and measuring the temperature of the snow cover.

The pit, sometimes called a hasty pit, has already been dug if the shovel shear test was used, which it probably has since a potential for danger has been evaluated already.

### *Slab Formation*

A pit's most significant use is to determine if slabs have formed. The slab's strength can range from soft new snow to rock-hard old snow. Avalanches do not require any special slab strength or type of snow. Remember, a relatively cohesive layer of snow must lie on a relatively weak, lubricating layer for a slab avalanche to occur.

The shovel shear test is simple and extremely important. More information can be gathered by slowly running a knife down through the snowpack and checking, more closely, for hard and soft layers. Brushing the side of the pit lightly with a gloved hand or, even better, a soft paintbrush will make hard and soft layers stand out.

The relative hardness of the slab can be determined with a simple test. Try to push your closed fist into the slab. If your fist sinks in with little effort, the slab is very soft. If the slab resists your fist, flatten your hand. If four fingers sink in with little effort, the slab is soft. If the slab resists four fingers, try your index finger. If your index finger sinks in, the slab is moderately hard. If one finger won't go in, but a pen or pencil will, the slab is hard. If it takes a knife, with little effort, to penetrate the slab, the slab is very hard. If the knife won't go in, the slab is ice. The harder the slab in relation to a soft layer beneath it, the greater the chance it will slide.

### Snow Cover Thickness

ET-metamorphism is encouraged by old, deep snow. The older the snow cover and the thicker the snow cover, generally, the more stable the snow cover. But deep snow may hide dangerous irregularities in the terrain. It will be unlikely that the total snow depth of deep snow can be measured without a probe pole, a lean strong pole that can be jammed down to the ground. A thin snow cover, say, three feet or less, encourages TG-metamorphism. TG snow is loose, remember, and will provide a sliding layer for later snowfall.

### Snow Crystal Types

Identifying crystal types requires a crystal screen, a magnifying glass, and a modicum of knowledge about their uses. The screen allows measurement of the size of the crystals by their relation to the lines on the screen. The magnifying glass allows this minute measurement and, also, determination of the structure of the crystals. Most people won't go to this bother. But a naked-eye look at the crystals is probably worth the effort. If small, rounded grains can be identified, the snow is older, more settled, more stable (although they can still form a slab over a very loose layer). If you see feather-like, cup-like, or scroll-like crystals, TG snow is being looked at. TG snow is always a sign of danger.

### Snow Temperature

Some of the effects of temperature changes on the snow cover are subtle and complex. Simple, informative tests can be performed in the pit, but they require a snow thermometer.

The temperature of the snow itself is important. Cold snow, snow well below freezing, metamorphoses slowly. Very low temperatures will keep the avalanche danger high for a long time. Warm snow, snow close to the melting point, changes rapidly, consolidating and shortening the duration of avalanche danger. Wet snow changes so quickly, especially if rain is falling, that avalanche danger can develop with incredible swiftness. Fortunately, wet snow avalanche danger tends to be short-lived, lasting usually only a matter of hours.

Large temperature gradients in the snow cover may also be important, although not as immediately important. If you note a big difference in temperature between the snow at the bottom and the top of the pit, the snow is tending toward instability. If the difference is small, the snow is tending toward stability.

## C. Weather Evidence

Remember, a storm can be either falling snow or windblown snow or a combination. To evaluate evidence relative to the weather, two things are of critical importance: how much snow has been deposited by the storm (quantity), and how fast was it deposited (intensity).

When the quantity approaches one foot in one storm, avalanche danger is certainly there. When the quantity approaches two feet in a single storm, avalanche danger is high. Any storm with deposition beyond three feet creates extreme avalanche danger in almost any terrain.

The faster the snow accumulates, the faster the danger accumulates. Heavy snowfall over several days does not stress the snow cover on slopes nearly as much as the same amount of snow in several hours. Generally, if the intensity of snow deposition is one inch or more per hour, avalanches are waiting to happen.

But if the snow is wet, then it is, of course, heavier, and the danger accumulates even faster. Snow can be measured by its water equivalency (the amount of water left if the snow is melted). Snowfall with a water equivalency of 0.1 inch per hour produces a high risk of avalanche. Water equivalency can be guessed by the type of snow crystals that are falling. Light snow, with soft feathery flakes, tends to stay put or slide off in loose sluffs. Balls of wet snow (graupel, sleet, hail) can build into dangerous slabs rapidly. As a rule, the more the snow "wets" the traveler, the more the snow is building toward avalanche proportions.

Even more than snowfall depth and intensity, it is wind that plasters avalanche-prone snow to leeward slopes. The wind velocity needed to move snow dangerously around varies with the wetness of the snow, but, as a guideline, by the time wind reaches the range of 10-15 miles per hour, it can move a substantial amount of snow. High winds of 15-40 mph will build avalanches from just about any snow type. Extreme winds, say beyond 50 mph, have two tendencies, depending on the amount of water in the snow. Cold, dry snow tends to be packed hard or blown away by extreme winds, leaving the avalanche danger relatively low. Wet snow and extreme winds will build slab avalanches quickly.

To sum up, the important rule is Watch the Wind's Direction and Speed. It determines which ridges will form cornices, which slopes will be loaded with snow, and, therefore, where avalanche danger will be highest.

An additional weather factor affecting avalanche formation is the air temperature, or, more specifically, changes in the air temperature. Falling temperatures tend to stabilize the snow cover. Rising temps tend to create more unstable snow deposits. But that is not always the case, especially if the temperature undergoes a sudden change. For example, a sudden drop in temperature puts additional stresses on slabs that have already formed, and can trigger a wet snow avalanche. Not long after the temperature drop, the snow will settle and the danger lessen. More dangerous, generally, is a sudden rise in temperature, a phenomenon which often provokes avalanches. If the rise reaches above freezing or produces rain, there will be an immediate and serious escalation in avalanche danger.

To sum up, the most important rule is Watch for Any Sudden Weather Change. Sudden snowstorms, sudden wind increases or shifts of direction, sudden rises or falls in air temperature, these things cause avalanches.

### D. Probable Outcomes of an Avalanche

What will be the probable outcome if the slope ahead avalanches and YOU are on it? The answer to this question is not technically "evidence," but no answer is more important to you. How thick is the snow cover? Has a slab formed? Does the slope ahead fan out or narrow down below you? Does it drop off a cliff, run into trees or rocks, or smooth out gently into a wide deposition zone? If you cross the slope ahead, and it avalanches, will you survive? Is it worth the risk?

### Safety Summary

OK, Sherlock, ready to decide? Evaluation of the hazard begins with the weather (subtle evidence), roams through the complex metamorphisms of the snowpack (indirect evidence), and culminates with the immediate conditions of the snow and terrain (directly observable evidence). The ability to decide, ultimately, is not gained in a seminar or from a book. As with the ability to respond medically, the skills are learned on the snowy slopes. And hazard evaluation is not a now-and-then thing for the traveler who wants to be safe. It needs to be a constant and integral part of the journey. Each step, each kick-and-glide, needs to be immersed in a larger awareness of all the nuances of the mountains. On some occasions you will hear the mountains shout their warnings: avalanches are thundering down all-around, six feet of snow fell overnight, a foot of depth hoar floods out of the hasty pit's wall. More often, and developing with experience, you will hear the mountains whisper their clues, evidence heard and interpreted only by astute listeners. Evaluation of the hazard, in the end, results from objective evidence and subjective "feeling."

# 6. FINDING THE SAFE ROUTE

"The point is whether one has got the heart to feel and the eyes to see. If he hasn't, his visits to the mountains are a pure waste of time . . . "

Lin Yutang, 1937.

Experience is a fine and heartless teacher. As with the experience of evaluating avalanche hazard, the experience of choosing the best route through avalanche country is best gained in the company of others who have greater experience, and a kinder heart. For your routefinding ability to mature, you must travel many different types of terrain in many different types of weather. Safe routefinding is a combination of choices made before the trip starts and choices made during the trip.

## Before the Trip

"All problems fall into one of two categories: trying to please others and trying to keep a schedule." Jed Williamson, 1985.

Who is going on the trip? The most basic of the Rules of Safe Travel is: Do Not Travel Alone. One of the most basic rules of happy safe travel is Choosing Companions Wisely. The best companions are 1) those who are enjoyable to be with, 2) those who know avalanche country and who have had similar experiences safely before, and 3) those who care enough to search vigorously if a party member is swept away.

And who is in charge? Small groups often travel safely and well without an acknowledged leader. Most groups function better with a leader, and the larger the group the greater the need for adequate leadership. The best leader is able to do two things: be extraordinarily safe, and lead without anyone knowing they are being led.

Who knows where and when the trip will end? Are they willing to send in a search party if you don't show up? And who should they send in? Have you checked to see what group will take on the responsibility of search-and-rescue if you need it?

And why is this trip being planned? Goals and objectives are far too often assumed and never stated, especially the objective of safety. Discussions on alternative routes, camping early, and, the most disagreeable of all decisions, turning back, are discussions best had in the comfort of a pre-trip planning room. Fun is wonderful objective, but it is, however, difficult to measure. Safety, on the other hand, is quite easy to measure . . . no one got hurt, no one got killed, no one got almost-killed. The trip may take a different route than planned and take longer than planned, but those are sometimes necessary choices. Coming back alive is, also, sometimes the result of a choice.

Where and when does the group plan to go? Know the route as completely as possible by either having gone before, going with someone who has, or gathering as much detail about the route as possible. Investigate the avalanche risk as completely as possible for that time of year. Some mountainous regions of the United States, and some in a few foreign countries, offer, as a public service, information and warnings about general avalanche danger (see Appendix). Specific information should be obtained from the nearest office of the Forest Service, Park Service, or Bureau of Land Management. If those offices can't help, and even if they can, more detailed info is often available from local ski areas, outdoor shops, newspapers, and radio stations.

The risk of an avalanche is usually rated as 1) low, it's OK to go, 2) moderate, go but be careful, 3) high, it's not very smart to go, and 4) extreme, it's really stupid to go. Remember, whatever the generally perceived risk of an avalanche, specific slopes may be ready to slide at any given moment and a rating of "low" never eliminates the chance of an avalanche.

What is being taken along? Your choice of gear and clothing should not be based on a general check list, but on the specific requirements of your trip's geography, time of year, length of days and miles, and number of participants.

There do seem to be a few things that the Wisdom of Safety would suggest. Even on day trips, extra food and water, extra clothing, and a sleeping bag and pad may save a life, or at least turn a totally miserable experience into an acceptably miserable experience. A repair kit suitable to the gear being used seems wise.

Gear specific to avalanche country should include a suitable shovel and an electronic rescue transceiver. Shovels are essential for hasty pits, emergency shelters, and recovering buried victims. Rescue transceivers, small devices that transmit and receive radio signals, give the best possible chance for recovery of a buried victim (see Chapter Seven). Other things to consider are an avalanche probe (a rod for "probing" the snow for a buried victim), avalanche cord (a bright-colored cord that trails out behind snow travelers which, in the event they are swept away, may lead to their burial ground), and, maybe, a snow saw (a wooden-handled, aluminum-bladed tool for cutting certain types of snow).

## During the Trip

"Decisions on safe route selection must be based upon facts and not upon assumptions." Tony Daffern, 1983.

The second of the Rules of Safe Travel is: Stay Away From Dangerous Areas. The most dangerous route of travel is one in which you may be the trigger for the avalanche. Stay off of avalanche release zones and stay out of avalanche paths. Stay off of leeward slopes and out from under cornices. Stay out of narrow ravines and slim valleys. Stay off of steep slopes, especially inclinations of 30 degrees or more, and very especially if the slope profile is convex. Thin stands of timber, where you can pass easily through, are thin enough for avalanches to pass easily through, and should be avoided. Remember, during and right after a big storm, all mountainous areas should be considered unsafe, and the colder the temperature the longer the hazard will persist.

Rule Two applies to rest breaks, photographic sessions, and lunchtime. If there is a potential danger, the risk rises the longer the party stays in the area, particularly the risk of a natural avalanche.

The Corollary to Rule Two is: don't camp or bivouac in an area of avalanche danger. Could the slope slide where the camp is planned? Could the slope above the camp slide? If a storm blows in, could the slope accumulate enough snow to slide? For travelers in avalanche terrain, it is wise to learn the skill of snow cave building. If the avalanche does occur, people in snow caves have a significantly better chance of survival than people in tents. Their chance of survival increases if they remembered to take their shovels into the cave.

**Figure 6-1** The safest rout is along a ridge.

The safest route of travel is on top of ridges, and toward their windward side, above avalanche release zones. The second safest route is down the middle of wide valleys, away from deposition zones. And thick stands of timber usually offer a bothersome but safe route.

The third basic Rule of Safe Travel is: never expose more than one person at a time to the possibility of an avalanche. Any buried victim has an excellent chance of living if un-buried quickly. Although statistics vary a little, a victim has a 75-80% chance of being successfully rescued in the first few minutes. After 30 minutes, the chance is down to around 50%. More than one-half of all successfully rescued victims had a body part or a piece of equipment visible above the snow. Time and distance under the snow keep lopping off survival time. A victim buried under six feet of snow is statistically dead. They simply can't be gotten out in time. A lot of people searching quickly gives one buried person the best chance of survival.

The Corollary to the Third Basic Rule is: travel at a speed that allows the person in front to always be easily visible to the person immediately behind. This is primarily to ensure that Rule Three works. But there is probably no better way to get into trouble in the wild outdoors, in any season, than traveling faster than the slowest member of the party. Struggling to keep up creates a cold, tired, careless, easily-lost person. Generally, parties travel more safely if they are, individually, about the same level of ability and experience, but this is certainly not a prerequisite for safety. The Rule is quite easy to keep if companions have been chosen wisely.

It is never safe to assume, just because the person in front made it across, that the next person will make it safely across a slope. In fact, a slope may tolerate a considerable amount of crissing and crossing before it slides down on a traveler.

Snow-covered mountains speak constantly in a subtle voice. Terrain, weather, the "feel" of the snow, the sound of the snow . . . in these are clues you learn to find through experience. You cannot eliminate risk, but you can find the safest route.

### Crossing a Dangerous Slope

When the route will cross a possible-avalanche slope, and evidence has been evaluated, and the verdict is "This is probably safe," you can do some things to further reduce the danger.

1) Think it over one more time. Is there an alternative route? If the slope does avalanche, what will the outcome be? Is it worth the risk? It is? OK, then...

2) Choose the safest route across the avalanche slope. Avoid the most likely trigger zones. Snow covers break off at points of greatest stress: near the top of a straight slope, at the steepest point of a convex slope, where an irregularity in the terrain (rocks, trees) breaks the snow surface. If the slope must be ascended or descended to gain the starting point of the safest route, go up or down on safe snow near the slope. If the dangerous slope itself must be ascended or descended to gain the safe starting point, follow the fall line instead of cutting across the fall line. This means go straight up or straight down the slope. If skis make this difficult, take them off and plow through the snow. If there are islands of safety on the slope, such as rock

outcroppings or dense stands of timber, plan a route from one of these to the next. On an open slope, stay high where, at least, there is less snow to slide down from above.

**Figure** 6-2 Route Across a Potential Avalanche Area

3) Traverse the slope diagonally, from the top toward the bottom, not horizontally. Horizontal cuts tempt the snow to slide more than diagonal cuts. And try to avoid turns which take you back under an already potentially-weakened slope. Ski turns especially add stress to the slope.

4) Loosen packstraps and undo hipbelts, unhitch safety straps on skis, loosen bindings on snowshoes and skis, and remove wrist loops on ski poles. Everything that an avalanche could catch and hold should be easy to shed.

5) Tighten up clothing, put on a hat, pull up the parka's hood, slip on mittens. Once caught in an avalanche, snow that gets inside of clothing cools the victim faster, shortening survival time.

6) Make sure electronic rescue transceivers are working, are turned to transmit, are secured somewhere on each person and not in a pack. Or be sure avalanche cord is strung out behind each person.

7) Cross one at a time, after everyone is ready, with at least one person serving as a spotter at all times. The spotter can yell if an avalanche breaks loose, watching the victim until he or she comes to rest or goes under. Generally, it is best for everyone to take the same trail across, but, with a large party, avoid following each other precisely, which cuts a deep trench through the snow, and may cut loose a slab. Don't stop until you have reached a safe spot.

If the party is carrying a rope, and a very secure belay point is available, and the dangerous slope is narrow enough, a belay may add safety. Since ropes can wrap around avalanche victims, or pull in other victims, they are, generally, considered more dangerous than safe on a wide slope.

## Safety Summary

Plan your trip well. Decide who is going, who is in charge, who will be available to come in and rescue you, where you're going, why you're going, and what you're taking. Know the avalanche forecast for your chosen route. Do not travel alone.

Once in the mountains, stay away from dangerous areas. Never expose more than one person at a time to avalanche danger. Travel at a speed that allows the person in front to be clearly visible to the person behind. Travel at the speed of the slowest person.

If you must cross a dangerous slope, plan the "safest" route across. Cross diagonally. Loosen all gear so that it can be shed quickly, and tighten all clothing. Be sure all rescue transceivers are turned to transmit. Play out avalanche cord. Appoint a spotter. Expose only one person at a time to the danger. Think it over one more time.

# 7. RESCUING THE VICTIM

"Avalanche rescue in the backcountry depends upon the actions of the unburied survivors." Tony Daffern, 1983.

If you are buried in an avalanche at a ski area, or some other organized commercial venture in snow country, professional help may respond quickly enough to save your life. In the domain of the backcountry skier, the snowshoer, the snowmobiler, the mountain climber, rescue will depend on other members of the party. Professional help will almost undoubtedly be useful only in an attempt to recover the body. Avalanche rescue can, then, be divided into three general areas: 1) self-rescue, 2) rescue by the party, and 3) rescue by an organized team.

## Self-Rescue

When the snow starts to slide, there may be time for you to quickly ski or run to the side of the avalanche path where snow is probably shallower and moving a little slower. The most direct route toward safety should be taken. Once the snow underfoot starts to break up, you will sink quickly into the churning mass, losing all hope of moving out of the avalanche. This would be a good time to scream. Screaming as loudly as possible alerts companions to your distress, and it may make you feel just a tiny bit better.

**Figure** 7-1 Run at a right angle from an oncoming avalanche.

If there are trees or rocks that can be grabbed and held on to, you should attempt to do so.

Once caught in the moving snow, all equipment that can be thrown off should be. Packs, skis, ski poles, and snowshoes become anchors dragging you under the frozen flood.

Swim. Although there is no officially-approved avalanche-swimming stroke, reverting to early attempts to stay-alive-in-water is the best plan. Dog paddling, treading wildly with legs and arms, anything to keep head above "water" should be used. If you feel your feet hit a hard surface, push off aggressively in an attempt to regain the surface. If your head goes under, you should keep your mouth shut, and not try to breath. A mouth or a nose full of snow will likely solidify enough to form a firm plug.

As the slide starts to slow down, you should make the most desperate of efforts to reach the surface. If that isn't working, vigorously try to create a breathing space by shaking your head, trying to get a hand up to your face to push the snow away, and wiggling around to make room for your chest to move. You should still keep your mouth shut while this is going on. While movement is still possible, one hand should be thrust toward the surface. Remember, most victims are found because something shows above the snow.

Now comes the hard part. Survival is more likely if you stay calm. The snow will quickly settle into the consistency of stone. Even partially-buried victims are often unable to dig themselves out without help. As the snow settles, efforts to get free waste priceless oxygen and valuable energy. Panic increases the need for oxygen. If unconsciousness descends, you should not try to fight it. Unconsciousness reduces the need for oxygen and the body's energy requirements.

## Rescue by the Party

Panic is ill-advised among the rescuers, also. It is the calm head that thinks appropriately. Two things are immediately critical: Where was the victim last seen as the snow pulled them along? Is the danger of more avalanching over? Someone should attach her eyes to the spot where the victim was last seen until that spot can be safely marked with something such as a ski or ski pole. Ideally, if there is danger of further avalanching, someone should be posted as a lookout to yell a warning.

Emergency situations tend to be handled much better under adequate leadership. A tense drama is suddenly unfolding and serious mistakes may be made. Leaders need to be sure not only that everything possible is being done for the victim, but also that everything possible is being done to keep the survivors safe. Rescuers will often take dangerous risks, and push themselves toward exhaustion and cold injury.

Going for help at this point would be a mistake. Remember how critical the first half-hour is! Even with only one rescuer, the first steps should include searching. A hasty search of the area should begin as soon as the snow has stabilized. Search at the last-seen spot, and on the slope below that spot. Mark spots where pieces of the victim's equipment are found. These may give further clues about where to search. If the victim was tied to an avalanche cord, look for its bright color. The surface gives the most important clues leading to the buried victim.

### The Probe

Which way was the victim most probably carried by the avalanche? Where are places a victim might have stuck on the way down? Victims will often lodge near where last seen, or on the uphill side of trees and rocks. With avalanche probes, or ski poles with the baskets removed, or skis, rescuers should probe in the most likely

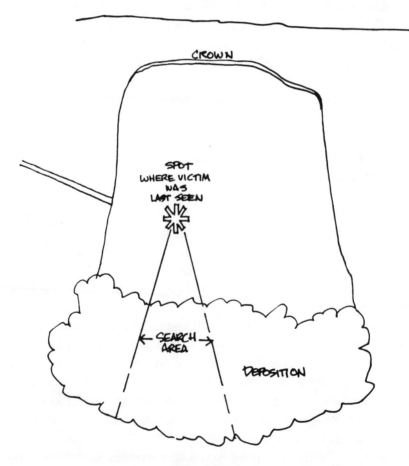

**Figure** 7-2 Concentrate search from spot where victim was last seen.

spots. Avalanche probes will go down twice as far as improvised probes, the advantage being obvious.

If the hasty probe search is non-productive, move to a more systematic probing search. Even two or three rescuers can systematically and quickly probe the highest priority areas. High priority should be given places where the slide debris is heaviest, to benches where the slope flattened before continuing on down, and to the slope below where pieces of equipment were found. Probe searches usually work best if they go up the slope, along the most likely descent line of the victim. Searchers should stand elbow to elbow, probe, step, probe, step. Or, with fewer searchers, they can stand far enough part to only touch outstretched hand to outstretched hand, probe right, probe left, step, repeat. When the probe hits a rock or frozen tree, the rescuer will feel the hardness of the object. It is a softer, giving feeling when the probe hits the victim. If the probe hits a buried victim, leave it in place and dig as rapidly as possible.

These quick probing searches are sometimes called coarse probes, and they sometimes find the victim. Very systematic, fine probes are usually used to recover a body.

## The Transceiver

If the victim was carrying a transceiver, the other units should immediately be turned to receive with the volume of each transceiver turned to full. To use rescue transceivers efficiently requires practice, but the basic procedure can be described. The search-with-a-transceiver will have two phases: a hasty search for the signal, and a detailed search for the burial point.

For the hasty search, rescuers should spread out, 30 to 40 feet apart over the highest priority area, and move in a line over that area. Everyone should stop every few paces to listen. It is difficult to hear clearly when crunchy walking-in-snow noises are everywhere.

A device will "peep" when it picks up the signal of its buried cousin. The transceiver will sound the loudest when its antenna is oriented toward the buried antenna. Unfortunately, this doesn't tell where the victim is. Once the signal is picked up, orient the transceiver in a position that gives the loudest "peep." This is done by turning the device in a circle, and moving it up and down through an angle of 90 degrees. The search needs to continue in a straight line with the transceivers held oriented in space in the same way. It is usually best, if a large group of searchers is working, to let one or two people continue the detailed search. Crowds get in the way, slowing the search down. Metal objects, such as ski poles and shovels, might deflect the signal, and should be kept out of the way.

The detailed search continues in the same straight line, transceiver still on full volume. As the signal grows louder, turn the volume down until the sound is barely audible, and continue walking. At the point where the sound almost disappears, a marker of some sort should be placed in the snow, and the searcher should turn back, 180 degrees, and retrace the same line of search, with the transceiver

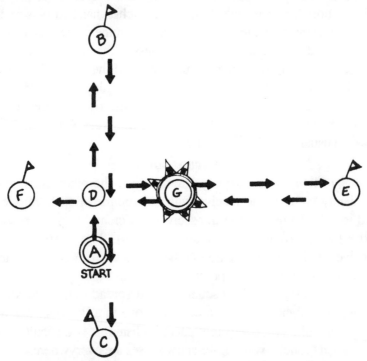

**Figure** 7-3 Pattern of transceiver search. Burial ground marked be G.

oriented the same way in space. The volume control should be left exactly where it is. The signal will increase, then start to fade. At the point where it starts to fade, a second marker should be placed. Now the middle point between the two markers should be marked.

At that middle point, the transceiver should be reoriented, at maximum volume, until the loudest signal is being received. Then the volume should be turned down until the sound is barely audible once again. Moving away from that point at a right angle to the original line of search, the detailed searcher will hear the signal increase in volume. Once again, the volume should be turned down until the sound can just be heard. That point should be marked. Another 180 degree turn, and a walk back along the second line, will bring the searcher to the point where the sound is barely audible again, and that point should be marked. The middle point of the second line of search will be close to the buried victim.

If the transceiver is oriented a third time in space to the loudest signal, and then moved back and forth over the burial area until the "peep" is strongest, the buried victim's transceiver can be located with reasonable precision. Probing the burial point might save some digging. Without probes, start digging immediately.

## A Cry for Help

At some point, you may decide that help is needed. Going for help should not be a mad rush for the nearest people, but it should be an organized search for assistance. A panicky cry for help is usually not in the best interest of the victim.

The best appeal for assistance is in writing. This reduces the high probability of the rescue team getting misinformation. In the interest of safety for those going for help, it is best to send two or three people out together.

Rescue teams like to know several things, if possible: 1) exactly when and where the avalanche occurred, with a map that has the avalanche spot marked, 2) what the geography of the general area is like, so they'll have a better idea about using a helicopter, snowmobile, etc., 3) what exactly happened to how many people, 4) how long it will take to access the accident area, 5) how the conditions are there and on the route to there, 6) how many people are on the scene already and how able they are to assist (do they have experience? what gear do they have?), 7) if victims have been found, what their condition is, and 8) anything else relevant.

Those going for help should know the route out and be equipped for a safe journey. They should stay close once the message is delivered, and be ready, if needed, to lead the rescue team back in.

The search-by-the-party should continue, if possible. Party members left behind still might find a buried victim in time.

### Rescue by an Organized Team

If the response of a rescue team is going to have any chance of success, which means a bring-them-back-alive rescue, the response must have several elements. First, it must be fast. There must be enough people, they must know what they're doing, they must have the right equipment, and, perhaps most important, they must have adequate leadership. All of these things imply that the team has done its preparation long before the accident. The successful team is well-trained, well-equipped, and ready . . . in short, they're well-organized. Knowing the basics of what a well-organized team will do may be of benefit if you find yourself involved in a search of your own. Remember, however, by the time the organized team arrives, the chance of finding a live victim is greatly reduced. The organized avalanche search-and-rescue will have two or three phases, depending on the length of the operation. Your search, with or without the response of an organized team, will be based on the same phases.

### Phase One

Because speedy location of the victim is the deciding factor in life or death, a hasty search team is usually sent out immediately. These people move light and fast, with minimum equipment and small numbers, hoping for a quick find. They will want to do the same things you, hopefully, have already done: mark the last-seen point, check the surface for clues, probe the high priority areas. They will perform a coarse probe because they know, from statistics, that coarse probes, even repeated several times, have a better chance of locating the victim than a fine probe.

If available, a dog trained for avalanche work will be brought in. Working with their noses, one avalanche dog can search about eight times faster than a 20-human team. Dogs rarely fail to locate victims if they are around six feet or less down, and they have sniffed out live victims more than 15 feet under the snow. Once the victim dies and cools off for an hour or so, dogs have trouble detecting the body. To make the dog's job easier, keep the search area clear of unnecessary gear and clothing, tobacco products, urine, food scraps, and such.

### Phase Two

By this time more searchers have arrived. These people will be carrying more equipment including sophisticated medical gear, food

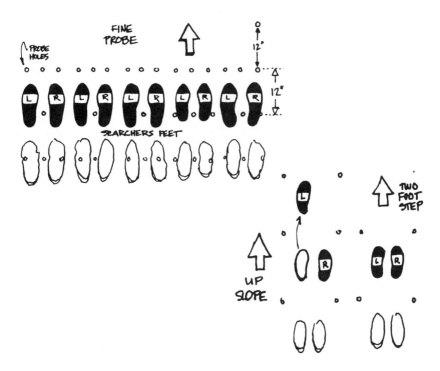

**Figure** 7-4 Coarse probe pattern (below). Fine probe pattern (above).

and shelter, and toboggans or some other form of transport for the victim. They will add their numbers to the coarse search if the leader thinks a chance of finding the victim alive still exists.

When the time for haste has passed, a fine probe may be used. Fine probes almost guarantee location of the victim. Fine probes will fail only if the victim is buried beyond the reach of the probes. Rescuers stand shoulder-to-shoulder and probe just in front of one foot, at the point between their toes, and just in front of the other foot. The line of rescuers takes one short step forward, about 12 inches, and repeats the three probes. Each step is ordered by a leader, so the search team is coordinated in its effort. It takes a 20-human team about four hours to fine probe an area approximately 100 yards by 100 yards.

Sometimes helicopters are used in avalanche rescue. Helicopters require relatively clear skies and relatively calm winds. They also need a relatively flat spot to land, preferably on a rise because they usually require some additional airspace for landing and taking off. If the snow cover is not firm, pilots like to have the snow surface packed down prior to landing. Rotor blades blow loose snow around, obscuring the pilot's vision. The landing zone (LZ) should be marked with something, preferably bright-colored, that is weighted enough to stay put in the disturbed air created by the helicopter. Everything else that might possibly be thrown up by the helicopter should be removed from the area. If there is a breeze, someone needs to stand, clearly visible to the pilot, with her back to the wind and her arms stretched forward, pointing the wind's direction.

Helicopters are a danger to rescuers. Stay where the pilot can see you. Never approach the helicopter unless the pilot signals you to do so, and never approach from the rear where the tail rotor is spinning invisibly fast. When approaching or leaving the helicopter, stay low and carry gear low.

## Safety Summary

If the snow starts to slide, rush to the side of the avalanche path. If caught, shed all gear and swim frantically, doing all possible to stay on top of the avalanche. If buried, hurriedly clear a breathing space around your face and chest, try to push a hand toward the surface, and try to stay calm.

If a member of your party is buried, don't panic and rush out for help. Mark the last-seen spot. Search quickly for clues on the surface. Probe the high priority areas. If you have transceivers, turn them to receive and start searching for the buried transceiver.

If you decide help is needed, send out an organized, written appeal. Send out two or three people with the appeal, and continue searching on your own. Be prepared to help the rescue team if they can use you.

# 8. CARING FOR THE AVALANCHE VICTIM

"Wilderness has no handrails, no telephones and no simple solutions for complex emergency situations." Tod Schimelpfenig and Linda Lindsey, 1991.

In two out of every three deaths by avalanche, the victim suffocates. Most of the remaining fatalities are the result of trauma, usually to the head and neck (cervical spine). Almost all living victims are suffering, to some extent, from shock and hypothermia, and they may have other injuries hidden inside their cold-weather clothing. They need to be transported out of the mountains. Immediate care of any avalanche victim involves 1) basic life support, and 2) stabilizing the cervical spine in case it has been injured, and 3) treatment for shock and cold injury. Extended care of the victim requires a complete check (assessment) for any other problems, treatment of the problems, prevention of further injury, and evacuation of the victim. None of this care can be neatly outlined, memorized, and followed exactly when needed. Each situation is different, every emergency unique. Sound judgement should lead to reasonable acts based on knowledge and experience.

## Basic Life Support

All haste should be made to uncover the buried victim's head first, being careful not to cut them up with your shovel in the rush to save them. It is usually quicker to dig from slightly downhill and angle in to a victim buried more than three or four feet down, since it's easier to shovel the snow out of the hole you're digging. As soon as his face is uncovered, clear his airway by removing any clumps of snow from his mouth and nose, and continue digging until his head, chest, and diaphragm are free. Open the victim's airway safely by stabilizing his head and neck with two hands while pushing up on the angle of his lower jaw with your index fingers (the jaw thrust), or by stabilizing the head with one hand and lifting the chin with the other (the chin lift). Check for breathing, and start mouth-to-mouth resuscitation, if needed.

**Figure** 8-1 Jaw Thrust

As digging continues, someone, ideally, should check for a carotid pulse. A great deal of effort should go into checking for a pulse. It is often very difficult to detect pulses in a cold victim, and failure to find one does not mean all hope is lost. Because cold, seemingly-lifeless victims are sometimes revived, you should follow the old adage that says: no one is dead until he is warm and dead.

When should cardiopulmonary resuscitation (CPR) be started? This is not an easy question to answer. There is a possibility the victim has a cold, rigid heart, beating weakly, but with enough energy to maintain life. A cold heart is fragile, and CPR will likely cause it to stop beating. And, if a victim has cooled to the point where his body has grown rigid, CPR won't work anyway. On the other hand, if he is dead and only semi-cold, CPR has an excellent chance of saving his life. Generally, if the victim has been buried less than two hours, and he is pulseless, CPR should be started, and continued as long as it doesn't create a risk to the rescuers. After two hours of burial, CPR will probably be either useless or more dangerous than helpful. Statistically, CPR seldom works on dead avalanche victims.

Although severe bleeding is uncommon in avalanche victims, they still deserve a check for life-threatening blood loss. Bleeding may be hidden deep inside bulky clothing, and the only way to check is to run your hands quickly underneath heavy parkas and sweaters. Also, large quantities of blood can virtually disappear if it runs down through the snow.

## Stabilizing the Cervical Spine

Conscious or unconscious, all victims should be removed from the snow gently. As mentioned, rough handling may stop a cold heart. Mismanagement of a damaged cervical spine carries the additional risk of turning a victim with an unstable neck into someone forever paralyzed... or dead. All avalanche victims have a broken neck until proven otherwise.

Ideally, one rescuer should hold the victim's head and neck stable while other rescuers take hold of the victim's body and move it as a unit, under direction of the head-holder, out of the snow. With a shortage of rescuers, do the best you can. Gentle dragging of the victim may be the safest option. Unfortunately, even in conscious victims, only X-rays can ultimately detect the presence or absence of spinal injury. The safest procedure is to improvise a cervical collar to hold the neck reasonably stable during the transport out. And, on the transport out, the victim should be secured to a rigid litter or toboggan to prevent further spinal damage.

## Head Injury

Sometimes head injuries are obvious, but the avalanche victim tends to demonstrate more subtle signs and symptoms indicating his brain is swelling inside of a very rigidly defined space, the cranium. If conscious, he may become increasingly disoriented, irritable, and combative... and, later, deeply unconscious. He may complain of a headache that keeps getting worse, and he may vomit repeatedly. His heart rate will slow down and increase in strength, and his breathing often become erratic. He may start to show unusual bruising around his eyes (if a slab hit him in the front of his head), or behind and below his ears (if the slab hit him from behind). He may complain of blurred vision, and his speech may become slurred. His walking might become unsteady. One pupil may grow obviously larger and less responsive that the other. He might have a convulsion.

Treat him as if he had a cervical spine injury, and try to keep his head slightly higher than his feet. If he is having difficulty breathing, start mouth-to-mouth breathing for him, ventilating him each time he tries to take a breath on his own. If a rescue team has arrived with supplemental oxygen, start a high-flow immediately. Rapid evacuation is critical. Unfortunately, patients with serious head injuries seldom do well when a hospital is far away.

## Shock

Expect all avalanche victims to demonstrate, to some extent, signs and symptoms of shock: rapid and weak heart rate, rapid and shallow respiratory rate, pale and cold skin (which is due, at least partially, to the snow), and an altered level of consciousness. Shock describes the condition of an inadequate flow of well-oxygenated blood. Injuries, pain, fear, and cold are all a part of the problem. Shock can kill, even long after the victim has been recovered from beneath the snow.

Field treatment for shock should include maintaining an open airway, getting the patient warm and dry, and positioning the patient with his feet slightly higher than his head. Avalanche victims are often dehydrated, which adds to the problems of shock and cold. If he is fully conscious, he may be given fluids, preferably warm fluids, but in small amounts. All treatment should be given in a calm and reassuring manner. Supplemental oxygen, once again, would be very beneficial. As you treat for shock, you are also treating for hypothermia.

## Hypothermia

You may also expect all avalanche victims to be suffering from hypothermia, a loss of body core temperature. Those who stay too cold for too long will have serious disturbances in the normal functioning of their bodies. Mild hypothermia causes loss of mental acuity, incoordination, and, as the victim's core temperature drops to around 95 degrees Fahrenheit, uncontrollable shivering. More profound hypothermia may result in a comatose patient with barely detectable, sometimes undetectable, pulse and respirations, and rigid muscles.

They often look dead. Profound hypothermia is not common in avalanche victims, however, since they more often die of suffocation or trauma before they cool off that much.

For all hypothermics, treatment includes getting them out of the wet and cold and into the warm and dry. First, get them out of the snow, preferably into some form of shelter and onto an insulating layer. Remove their clothing, gently, and bundle them up in thick insulation: dry clothing, sleeping pads, other people. A radiation barrier, such as a sheet of plastic, space blanket, or a tent's fly, as a final wrap, will ensure retention of as much body heat as possible. The resultant cocoon is sometimes referred to as a "hypothermia wrap." Chemical heat packs or warm water bottles, placed inside the "wrap" at strategic areas of their body (neck, armpits, groin, palms of the hands, soles of the feet), will do much to help them rewarm. If they are conscious, fix them something warm to drink.

Unconscious hypothermics, especially those that seem dead, require very gentle handling. Remember, they are fragile from the cold. They should be treated with the same hypothermia wrap. But don't try to force warm drinks down their throats. Of great benefit

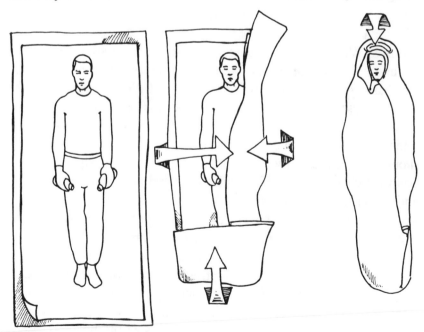

**Figure** 8-2 Hypothermia Wrap

would be a high-flow of warmed, humidified oxygen, but you won't have that unless a rescue team has arrived. If the severely hypothermic patient seems breathless, start mouth-to-mouth breathing. Your personal low-flow of warmed, humidified oxygen will help.

## Frostbite

Frostbite is frozen tissue in a localized part of the body. It can be very superficial, involving only skin, or very deep, involving bone. Frostbitten tissue is cold, pale or white or gray, and stiff. As freezing goes deeper, the tissue becomes stiffer and stiffer until, finally, it is rock hard. Superficial frostbite, where the skin depresses easily when gently pushed, should be rewarmed immediately with passive skin-to-skin contact. Deep, hard frostbite should be rewarmed in a stable environment through immersion in warm water. Do not attempt this in the field. Patients with hard frostbite almost always do better if the injury is wrapped with dry insulation and left for a physician to manage in a controlled environment. For any frostbite injury, do not rub it and do not put it near an open flame or any other high heat source. For any frostbite that has thawed, protect it carefully from being injured or refrozen.

## Assessment

A breathing, pulsing victim needs to be checked over for other injuries. When this takes place depends on unpredictable factors including the basic life support requirements (you may never get to do a full assessment because you're busy doing CPR), the severity of the weather, and the number of rescuers. Assessments should go from head to foot. Squeeze bones, move joints gently, look for cuts and bruises, check for anything that hurts or feels abnormal. Your survey should not unnecessarily expose the victim to the cold. In some cases, you may choose to identify injuries only and postpone treating them until the victim has been warmed.

A check should be made of vital signs, especially level of consciousness, heart rate, respiratory rate, and skin condition. A normal person will be able to answer questions reasonably, particularly questions in reference to who, what, when, and where. Normal heart rates range from 60 to 80 strong beats per minute, and normal respiratory rates from 12 to 20 unlabored breaths per minute. Skin, in the non-pigmented areas (i.e., mucus linings of the lips and eyes), should be pink and moist. Changes in vitals don't tell you what's wrong, but they do indicate changes in the condition of the victim. Changes toward normal are healthy, and changes away from normal are unhealthy.

## Treatment of Injuries

Unstable and painful bones and joints should be well-padded and splinted. Open wounds should be cleaned, dressed, and bandaged. Secure splints and apply bandages snugly, but loose enough to allow healthy circulation. Restricted circulation makes an already cold victim especially susceptible to frostbite.

## Prevention of Further Injury

Once stabilized, victims should be monitored carefully for any changes in their condition. The less alert they are, the more carefully they need watching. Not only their injuries need monitoring, but also their body temperature, fluid needs, and food needs. They may require help in attending to their bodily functions.

Do not underestimate your patients need for psychological support. Often the greatest good can be achieved with the warmth of human understanding . . . not a cheerleader and not a detached observer, but someone in-between, someone who quietly and confidently lifts the spirits of the avalanche victim.

## Evacuation

Transport of the avalanche victim is the final stage of care. Transport begins with the determination what type of evacuation will be required. Can the victim walk or ski out? Can you carry the victim on your back? Is your party large enough and strong enough to do a safe carry? Can you improvise a litter or a sled to move the victim in?

Figure 8-3 Evacuation of the victim... the final step.

Do you have enough equipment and food to support the group during the evacuation? Would it be wiser to send for more help instead of trying to self-evacuate? Who will you ask for help? Are helicopters or snowmobiles available in your area? The answers to these questions will determine how you get your victim out.

## Safety Summary

Once located and removed from the snow, avalanche victims require immediate attention to their basic life support systems: airway, breathing, circulation. Priority attention should be given to their cervical spines, and to the possibility of head injury, shock, and hypothermia. An assessment should be made of their condition, and treatment given for all noted and suspected injuries. They should be monitored in order to prevent, if possible, a worsening of their condition. Pay special attention to their need for an adequate airway, for maintenance of body heat, for food and fluid needs, and for psychological support. Evacuate the victim as soon as it is safely possible.

# 9. GEARING UP FOR AVALANCHE SAFETY

Safety out in the mountains during the season of avalanches begins before you ever leave the safety of your home. Decisions must be made about who is going where to do what. Who is in charge? How long is the trip? What is the worst weather you can expect during that time period? Who is available to come to your aid if you need help? Each journey will have specific needs and not-needs. But some general suggestions can be made for all snow season trips.

For maximum safety, each individual should carry:

1. Extra food (especially food with a lot of energy to the bite).

2. Extra clothing (including spare socks, cold-weather hat, and a heavy parka suitable for just standing around).

3. Cold-weather sleeping bag and pad (try them out close to home before your life depends on it).

4. Headlamp (and spare batteries).

5. Snow shovel (a metal one with at least a 12 inch blade, and preferably a D-shaped handle. Small folding shovels and lightweight plastic shovels move avalanched snow inadequately.)

6. Avalanche probe (or, at least, an avalanche-probe ski pole).

7. Rescue transceiver (and be sure the one you're carrying is compatible with those being carried by your companions).

8. Avalanche cord (if you can't afford a transceiver, and pick a bright color).

9. Portable two-way radio (sometimes impractical, but if they're available you get an extra-bonus safety margin).

For maximum safety, the group should carry:

1. Cold-weather shelter (enough for everyone to be able to bed down in reasonable comfort).

2. Medical kit (including material for splinting and bandaging, and emergency heat packs).

3. Sheet of plastic 10 x 10 feet (or something similar that can be used in a "hypothermia wrap").

4. Portable stove (and extra fuel).

5. Pots (of a size suitable for melting snow for drinking water for everyone).

6. Repair kit (including tools and materials to fix all the necessary gear you have with you).

7. Sled (or materials to improvise a sled out of the gear you have with you).

8. Snow saw (for an easier time with the shovel shear test, and emergency igloo building).

9. Climbing rope (that can be used to weave a litter, belay travelers over steep slopes, belay a victim down steep slopes).

# 10. GOING BEYOND THE BASICS

Further reading.

(The) ABC of Avalanche Safety, by E. R. LaChapelle, The Mountaineers, Seattle, Washington, 1985. (Short, non-technical handbook for mountain travelers.)

Avalanche Awareness (a video), from Alliance Communications, Inc., Denver, Colorado, 1988. (A 30-minute videotape for backcountry travelers on the fundamentals of avalanche safety.)

Avalanche Handbook, by R. Perla and M. Martinelli, Jr., US Department of Agriculture, Forest Service, Washington, D.C., 1976. (Government-printed, technical text directed toward avalanche evaluators.)

(The) Avalanche Hunters, by Montgomery M. Atwater, Macrae Smith Company, Philadelphia, Pennsylvania, 1968. (Good source of information on the history and methodology of avalanche forecasting.)

Avalanche Safety for Skiers and Climbers, by Tony Daffern, Rocky Mountain Books, Calgary, Alberta, 1983. (Highly readable resource for the backcountry skier/mountaineer.)

Avalanches and Snow Safety, by Colin Fraser, Charles Scribner's Sons, New York, 1978. (Good resource for the backcountry traveler, based on experiences in Europe.)

Field Guide to Snow Crystals, by Edward R. LaChapelle, University of

Washington Press, Seattle, Washington, 1969. (Easy-to-use pocket
guide to identification of snow crystals.)
Mountaineering - Freedom of the Hills, fourth edition, edited by Ed
Peters, The Mountaineers, Seattle, Washington, 1982. (Chapters on
travel in avalanche country and mountain weather.)
Snow, by Ruth Kirk, William Morrow and Company, New York, 1978.
(A non-technical, poetically written look at many aspects of the white
world.)
Snow Avalanche Sites, their identification and evaluation, by M.
Martinelli, Jr., US Department of Agriculture, Forest Service,
Washington, D.C., 1974. (Government bulletin describing avalanche-
prone areas.)
Snow Crystals/Les cristaux de neige, by R. Perla, National Hydrology
Research Institute, Inland Waters Directorate, Ottawa, Canada, 1978.
(Government bulletin, with color photographs, on crystals and their
changes within the snowpack.)
Snow Sense - A Guide to Evaluating Snow Avalanche Hazard, by Jill
Fredston and Doug Fesler, Alaska Department of Natural Resources,
Division of Parks and Outdoor Recreation, 1984. (Understandable,
quick-reference guide to hazard evaluation.)
Understanding Avalanches, by B. Diltz-Siler, Signpost Publications,
Lynnwood, Washington, 1977. (Guide to safety in the Cascades and
Sierras.)
Training/Seminars.
Alaska Avalanche School, Alaska Department of Natural Resources,
Division of Parks and Outdoor Recreation, Pouch 7-001, Anchorage,
AK 99510.
American Avalanche Institute, Inc., Box 308, Wilson, WY 83014.
National Avalanche School, 2638 Dapplegray Lane, Walnut Creek,
CA 94596.
Sierra Avalanche Seminars, P. O. Box 8010, Truckee, CA 95737.

# APPENDIX: AVALANCHE FORECAST CENTERS*

ALASKA, Anchorage: (907) 271-4500.

ALBERTA, Banff: (403) 762-3600, or Calgary: (403) 247-1910.

CALIFORNIA, Mammoth Lakes: (714) 934-6611, or Truckee: (916) 587-2158.

COLORADO, Aspen: (303) 920-1664, or Colorado Springs: (303) 520-0020, or Denver/Boulder: (303) 236-9435, or Dillon: (303) 468-5434, or Fort Collins: (303) 482-0457, or Vail: (303) 827-5687.

IDAHO, Ketchum: (208) 622-8027.

MONTANA, Whitefish: (406) 257-8606.

OREGON, Bend: (503) 382-6922, or Portland: (503) 221-2400.

UTAH, Logan: (801) 752-4146, or Ogden: (801) 621-2362, or Provo: (801) 374-9770, or Salt Lake City: (801) 364-1581.

WASHINGTON, Seattle: (206) 527-6677, or Snowqualmie Pass: (206) 442-7669.

WYOMING, Teton Village: (307) 733-2664.

*Information usually available from December to April. These numbers are subject to change. Contact your local forecast center, ranger district office, park service office, or ski area for up-to-date information.

# INDEX